SMALL ARMS

IDENTIFICATION SERIES

.303 RIFLE, No. 1, S.M.L.E.

Marks III and III*

Parts Identification & Lists, S.M.L.E. Series Notes,

Exploded Parts Drawings, Descriptions,

Accessories & Fittings.

S.A.I.S.
No. 1

Ian Skennerton

REFERENCES:

'Accurizing & Shooting Lee-Enfields' *Ian Skennerton & Brian Labudda* 2005
'Australian S.M.L.E. Variations' S.A.I.S. #19 *Skennerton* 2004
'Identification List' *Australian Military Forces* 1945, M.G.O.
'Identification Manual, .303 British Service Cartridge' *Barry Temple* 1986, TEMPLE
'List of Changes in British War Material — 1900-1910' *Ed. Skennerton* 1987
'List of Changes in British War Material — 1910-1918' *Ed. Skennerton* 1994
'List of Changes in British War Material — 1918-1926' *Ed. Skennerton* 1998
'List of Changes in British War Material — 1926-1940' H.M.S.O.
'Text Book of Small Arms — 1904' H.M.S.O.
'Text Book of Small Arms — 1929' H.M.S.O.
'The Lee-Enfield Story' *Ian Skennerton* 1993, SKENNERTON
'.303-inch Machine Guns and Small Arms — 1917' Ordnance College, H.M.S.O.

ACKNOWLEDGMENTS:

Brian Labudda, Lee Spares, Kingaroy, Australia
Robert Courtney, Australian War Memorial, Canberra, Australia
The Trustees, Australian War Memorial, Canberra, Australia

National Library of Australia
Cataloguing-in-Publication data:
Skennerton, Ian D.
ISBN 0 949749 19 2

Typesetting, layout and design by Ian D. Skennerton.
Published by Ian D. Skennerton, P.O. Box 80, Labrador 4215, Australia.
Printed and bound by Thai Watana Panich Press Co. Ltd., Rama 1 Rd., Bangkok, Thailand.

Distributors:

North America—
Arms & Militaria Press
PO Box 5014
Grants Pass
OR 97527
USA

Great Britain—
Jeremy Tenniswood
36 St. Botolphs St.
Colchester
Essex CO2 7EA
England

Australia—
Ian D. Skennerton
PO Box 80
Labrador
Qld. 4215
Australia

Website: www.skennerton.com
E-mail: idskennerton@hotmail.com

CONTENTS

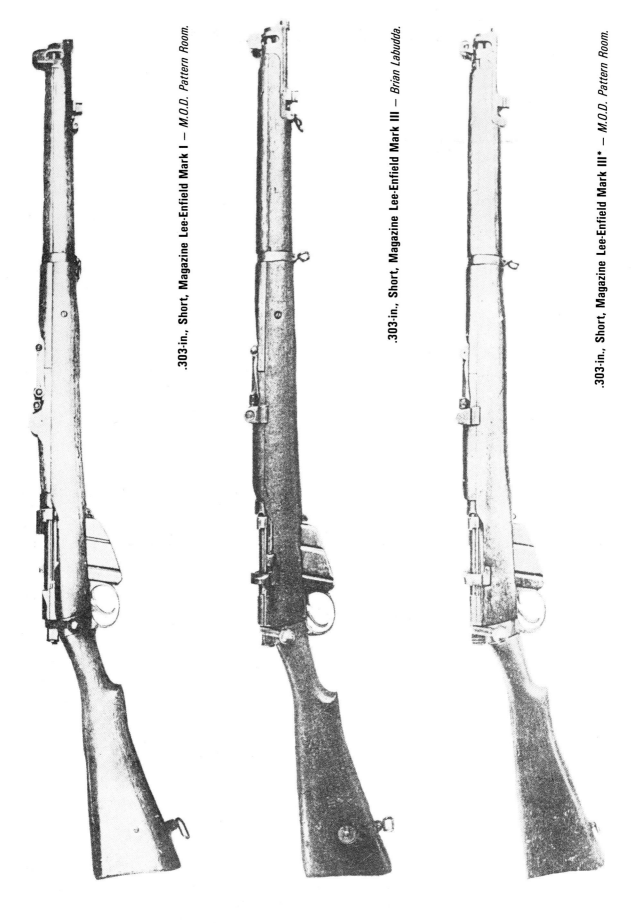

.303-in., Short, Magazine Lee-Enfield Mark I — *M.O.D. Pattern Room.*

.303-in., Short, Magazine Lee-Enfield Mark III — *Brian Labudda.*

.303-in., Short, Magazine Lee-Enfield Mark III* — *M.O.D. Pattern Room.*

.303 RIFLE, No. 1 S.M.L.E.

Marks III & III*

S.M.L.E. RIFLE GENEALOGY

The principal criticisms levelled at the .303 Magazine Lee-Enfield rifle during the Boer War in South Africa were the need for a charger loading facility and its considerable length. Two patterns of a new modified Lee-Enfield rifle were tested in 1901, one with Speed and Watkin's patent charger-loading system, as eventually adopted on the Mark I Short Magazine Lee-Enfield. But both these rifles were still fitted with the long, 30.2-in. M.L.E. barrel. Then one of these rifles was shortened by five inches to see if handling and balance were suitable and if the length was acceptable to both infantry and cavalry units, making carbines unnecessary for the specialist mounted units.

Later in 1901, 1,055 "Shortened Enfield Modified Rifles" were made at the Enfield Royal Small Arms Factory, based upon the No. 1 Modified Rifle, shortened. These incorporated more recent improvements, notably a safety catch fitted on the action body, and an inner barrel band. Trials of the new short rifle early in 1902 resulted in recommendations for its universal adoption, a uniform length arm for all services. The new trials rifle was 4.5 inches longer than the cavalry carbine but 5 inches shorter than the long rifle. It weighed only 8 oz. more than the carbine but 1 lb. 8 oz. less than the M.L.E. rifle.

The .303 Short, Magazine Lee-Enfield Rifle Mk I was first approved on 23rd December 1902. However, some minor changes which included the addition of windage adjustment on the backsight, resulted in its being re-introduced in the List of Changes a few months later, with an eventual official introduction date of 1st January 1904. A comprehensive description and the appropriate particulars of the trials and short rifle development are recorded at the beginning of Chapter 5 in the *Lee-Enfield Story.*

In keeping with routine British procedure, the first .303 Short, Magazine Lee-Enfield (S.M.L.E.) model was designated the **Mark I**. This pattern was produced at Enfield, B.S.A. and L.S.A., but not manufactured outside Britain. A **Converted Mark II** model introduced along with the Mark I rifle was merely the superseded Magazine Lee-Metford Marks II or II* or Lee-Enfield Marks I or I* rifle converted and upgraded to the new Mark I S.M.L.E. configuration.

The **Mark I*** was introduced in 1906. Most of these were produced at R.S.A.F. Enfield, although some have been noted with B.S.A. and Sparkbrook markings. The Indian Ishapore rifle factory commenced manufacture of the Mark I* model in 1908 also. The **Converted Mark II*** was a Lee-Metford Mark II or II*, or Lee-Enfield Mark I or I* rifle rebuilt to S.M.L.E. Mark I* specifications.

The **Mark III** S.M.L.E. was introduced in 1907 and it was the principal British and Empire service rifle of the Great War. Production of this model was commenced at Ishapore in 1909 and at Lithgow in Australia in 1913. These rifles are marked with the factory name and year of manufacture on the right side of the receiver, on the butt socket. The **Converted Mark IV** was a factory conversion of the Lee-Metford Mark II or II*, or Lee-Enfield Mark I or I* rifle to S.M.L.E. Mark III configuration.

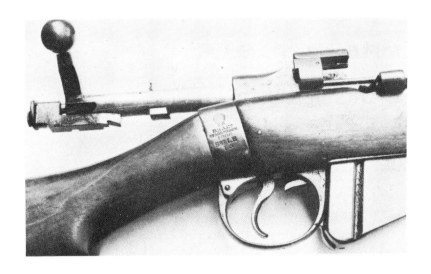

Mark I* S.M.L.E. with the bolt open, in loading position; note charger guide position on the bolthead and early style cocking piece. Receiver markings, R.H. side of butt socket. *B. Labudda.*

S.M.L.E. Mark I & I* series backsight. Steel rearsight protector mounts on the rear handguard. Sight bed screws onto the barrel, not fitting around it. *B. Labudda.*

Mark III & III* S.M.L.E. series rifles have the charger-guide bridge across action body. Bolt closed. Early cocking piece has knurled rim at back. *B. Labudda*

Later style of backsight cap on Mk III* rifle; notice the "waisted" shoulder of its front edge, which butts up against the leaf proper. Rearsight protector wings are mounted onto the fore-end, not the rear handguard as on Mark I S.M.L.E. series rifles. *B. Labudda*

The converted S.M.L.E. models may seem a little confusing to understand or to identify at first. The Converted Mark II series and the Converted Mark IV were all marked on the left side of the action body on the butt socket, and thus may be readily identified. However, the Marks I** and I*** merely had additional asterisks stamped after the original designations on the right side of the butt socket.

The upgraded S.M.L.E. patterns were:

Rifle, SMLE	Converted from:	Upgraded to:
Mk I** ...	SMLE Mk I	Some features of SMLE Mk III
Mk I*** ...	SMLE Mks I*, Mk I**	Mk VII ammunition sighting
Cond. Mk I ...	MLM Mk I*	SMLE Mk I
Cond. Mk II ...	MLM Mks II, II* or MLE Mks I, I*	SMLE Mk I
Cond. Mk II* ...	MLM Mks II, II* or MLE Mks I, I*	SMLE Mk I*
Cond. Mk II**	SMLE Cond Mk II	Some features of SMLE Mk III
Cond. Mk II***	SMLE Cond Mk II*	Some features of SMLE Mk III
Cond. Mk IV ...	MLM Mks II, II* or MLE Mks I, I*	SMLE Mk III

Manufacturing economies resulted in the **Mark III*** being introduced in 1915, although official approval for this new version was not given until 1916. B.S.A. was first to produce the Mark III*, followed soon afterwards by Enfield. Manufacture of the Mark III* was commenced at Lithgow in about 1918. India appears to have produced the Mark III until the 1930's before advancing to the Mark III*. The advance from Mark III to III* did not always conform with definite patterns, it was more of a transition. Some Mark III* rifles may be found with provision for the cut-off, or even the earlier type of sights. The Mark III* was a manufacturing economy and in some cases, the Mark III model was reverted to for a short time after the Great War finished.

S.M.L.E. rifle production in India resulted in a number of special types. Because many of the Indian patterns did not correspond exactly with their British service equivalents, the designation 'I.P.' (India Pattern) was appended in their official M.L.E. and S.M.L.E. nomenclature in many cases. Few such examples are encountered today in their original form as most Indian rifles were later 're-manufactured' and remarked to correspond with the typical Marks III and III* models. See the *Lee-Enfield Story* pages 331-345 for a comprehensive study of the Indian production.

In Australia, the S.M.L.E. Marks III and III* were the only .303 Lee-Enfield models manufactured for general issue; these Lithgow rifles correspond with the typical British patterns. During World War 2, the Australian production was transferred to subsidiary rifle factories at Orange and Bathurst, however, the receiver butt sockets are still marked 'MA LITHGOW' on the right side. British, Australian and Indian proof and view marks on component parts are different. These are illustrated in the *Lee-Enfield Story*, pages 479-495, and in *The Broad Arrow - British Empire markings (Skennerton)*.

To remedy certain shortcomings of the leaf sights and its comparatively short sighting radius, aperture sights were recommended for the next model of service rifle. An outer band at the rear of the nosecap served to strengthen the nosecap assembly for bayonet work. These particular improvements were incorporated in the limited production **Mark V** trials rifle which was produced at Enfield between 1922 and 1924. The Mark V never went into general service. On this model, long range dial sights were deleted although the magazine cut-off was retained.

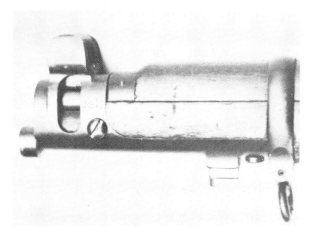

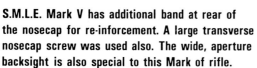

S.M.L.E. Mark V has additional band at rear of the nosecap for re-inforcement. A large transverse nosecap screw was used also. The wide, aperture backsight is also special to this Mark of rifle. Note the "V" stamp and angled thumb grooves on the safety catch locking bolt. *M.O.D. Pattern Room*

In 1926, British Service small arms nomenclature was changed from Mark and "*" variation to a Number, Mark and "*". So the Rifle Mark III became **Rifle No. 1 Mark III** and the Mark III* became **Rifle No. 1 Mark III***. This system was similarly applied to bayonets, pistols, other small arms and their related stores. As the .303 rifle became Rifle No. 1, the .22RF Lee-Enfield trainers were designated Rifle No. 2. The .303 Pattern 1914 rifle became Rifle No. 3.

The last model of the No. 1 rifle series was the **No. 1 Mark VI**, a trials model circa 1930. This model retained the aperture sights and even the magazine cut-off, but it was more specifically designed for modern production techniques. The action body is slab sided and the new style of fore-end, nosecap and bayonet attachment laid the foundations for the succeeding No. 4 rifle model. Production of the Mark VI was limited and it was not a general issue.

During the 2nd World War, Royal Ordnance Factory rifle production in Britain was concentrated upon the No. 4 Mark I model. But the No. 1 rifle continued to be manufactured at the original B.S.A. Small Heath factory in central Birmingham. German bombing of the plant caused this rifle production to be dispersed and so some different forms of factory markings may be noticed on the butt sockets (*Lee-Enfield Story* pages 176-177). The No. 1 rifle production in Britain was terminated before the end of the war.

However, production of the No. 1 (S.M.L.E.) rifle continued in Australia and India after it was discontinued in England. Although Australian manufacture of the No. 1 rifle ceased at the end of the war, a machinery trials batch of 1,000 rifles was made at S.A.F. Lithgow in the early 1950's. These Lithgow action bodies are dated 1953, ending with the serial number F40580. So the total run of S.M.L.E. rifles from 1913 amounted to 640,580.

Indian .303 rifle manufacture continued after the war, probably until 1963 when a special 7.62mm model, the 7.62mm 2A, was introduced. This utilised a higher grade of steel to accommodate the more powerful NATO cartridge. The 2A was manufactured until 1970 and represents the final S.M.L.E. rifle production after nearly seventy years.

.303 S.M.L.E. MODEL IDENTIFICATION TABLES

A comparative listing of the principal .303 Short Magazine Lee-Enfield rifle Mark and "*" variations is provided here with brief descriptions, along with their introduction years and notable modifications and improvements. This only applies to the original Short Magazine Lee-Enfield, or what became referred to as the Rifle No. 1 from 1926. The Rifles No. 4 and No. 5 and subsequent .22 Nos. 7, 8 and 9 trainers utilised a later style, strengthened action body and are therefore not included here.

S.M.L.E. model	Intro- duced	Principal features	Body mark	Other notes	LoC para	L.E.S. pages
Mk I	1903	The new short rifle. Shorter 25.2-in. barrel, charger-loading guides on bolthead and left side of action body.	R.H.	Early model had one spring on rear handguard, then changed to two springs. Also fitted, new windgauge.	11715, 11947	107-117, **398**
Mk I*	1906	Brass buttplate with butt trap, swivel mount inletted into butt.	R.H.	Like Mk I SMLE, except for buttplate and sling swivel.	13577	115-117, **401**
Mk I**	1908	Converted SMLE Mk I to include some Mk III features.	R.H.	Naval conversion. Most were later modified at Enfield. †	14936	134-135, **404**
Mk I***	1914	Modified SMLE Mk I* & I** for Mk VII ammunition.	R.H.	Sight bed mods. Can be with or without charger bridge.	16910	139-140, **402**
Mk I Cd.	1903	Converted MLM Mk I* to Mk I SMLE configuration.	L.H.	Samples only, no production for service.	11948	111-112, **399**
Mk II Cd.	1903	Converted MLM/MLE to Mk I SMLE configuration.	L.H.	Similar to Mk I SMLE, but converted from earlier models.	11949	112-113, **400**
Mk II* Cd.	1906	Converted MLM/MLE to Mk I* SMLE configuration.	L.H.	Similar to Mk I* SMLE, but converted from earlier models.	13578	115-116, **401**
Mk II** Cd.	1908	Converted SMLE Mk II to include some Mk III features.	L.H.	Naval conversion. Most were later modified at Enfield. †	14936	134-135, **404**
Mk II*** Cd	1909	Converted SMLE Mk II* to include some Mk III features.	L.H.	Naval conversion. Most were later modified at Enfield. †	14936	134-135, **405**
Mk III	1907	Charger bridge across top of body, over the boltway.	R.H.	Has new type nosecap wings, backsight & handguards.	13853	118-167, **403**
Mk III*	1915	Has no volley sights or backsight windage adjustment.	R.H.	Magazine cut-off slot also omitted soon afterwards.	17622	141-167, **407**
Mk IV Cd.	1907	Converted MLM/MLE to Mk III SMLE configuration.	L.H.	Similar to Mk III SMLE, but a conversion.	13854	120-139, **403**

S.M.L.E. model	Introduced	Principal features	Body mark	Other notes	LoC para	L.E.S. pages
Mk V	1922	Trials rifle only, not introduced into general service.	R.H.	About 20,000 made at Enfield, between 1922 and 1924. Dated as such on the receiver body.	none	168-169, **408**
Mk VI	1930	Trials rifles only, not introduced into general service	L.H.	1,025 made at Enfield, between 1930 and 1933. Dated as such on the L.H. side of butt socket.	none	173-175, **411**

Signs, Abbreviations & Column Headings:—

†   *Later conversion at Enfield saw many fitted with the charger bridge and Mk III rifle bolthead. The nosecap ears were also "drawn out" and "straightened".*

Cd.   *A compression of "Converted". The official abbreviation "Cond." is often found stamped on these rifle conversions alongside the particular Mark designation.*

Introduced   *The year of introduction into the British service, and usually, this was the first year of production. Official dates of approval, per the List of Changes, rarely coincide with the month of introduction or commencement of manufacture.*

Body mark   *Indicates the position of manufacture or conversion stamps on that particular model or conversion. This was marked on the receiver (action body) at the butt socket. In the case, say, of a converted Mark II* rifle, the factory, year of conversion and "Sht L.E. Cond. II*" stamp will be located on the left side of the butt socket. In this particular instance, though, the original M.L.E. or M.L.M. marks will still be evident on the right side of the receiver butt socket, for example, "ENFIELD 1896 L.E. and I.", because this was the original rifle from which the conversion was made. Some .22 training conversions were later modified from .303 converted rifles, and so three sets of markings may be encountered on some of the sub-calibre trainers.*

LoC para   *Listing of the paragraph reference number in "List of Changes in British War Material and Military Stores" (Ed. Skennerton), Vol. III (1900-1910) or Vol. IV (1910-1918). Full details of the particular changes and alterations will be found here. Vol. V (1918-1926) with a master index for the 5-volume series is due to be published in 1994.*

L.E.S. pages   *Lists the appropriate text reference pages and description in the "Lee-Enfield Story". The page reference number in bold type denotes the page number for the illustrated details in Chapter 12, the Rifle Descriptions. Also check pages 481-482 for examples of the various action body markings.*

Note:— The "Rifle No. 1" nomenclature was only applied after 1926, so the earlier Marks which were obsolete or omitted from service vocabulary by this time should not be so named. Thus, it would be improper or incorrect to refer to the .303 S.M.L.E. Mark I as the Rifle No. 1 Mark I, or to the .303 Converted Mark IV as the Rifle No. 1 Mark IV. The list of rifles involved in this 1926 change and those rifles retained in store but omitted from Vocabulary, will be found on page 172 of the *Lee-Enfield Story*.

DIFFERENCES IN COMPONENT PARTS

This section describes and illustrates the differences found in major component parts of the four most common S.M.L.E. rifle models. Should a particular rifle being examined, rebuilt or restored not come under any of these four categories, check with the tables on the previous pages to ascertain which model it should resemble or conform with most. Also read the original references in the List of Changes and the *Lee-Enfield Story* as indicated in the previous two pages.

Rifle designation markings on the butt socket will show the rifle mark or type. Or should certain parts be on hand for identification, check through the following six pages to classify them. Should they not be shown in this section, the Parts Identification List on pages 22 to 39 will most likely illustrate and name them correctly.

For the S.M.L.E. rifles, the mark designation is also often found stamped on the right side of the wooden buttstock, underneath the maker's roundel. Butts of the Marks I, I* and III .303 short rifle series were marked with the manufacturer's roundel. These should usually correspond with the factory name stamped into the butt socket of the action body. Such examples are illustrated on pages 478, 488 and 489 of the *Lee-Enfield Story*. Butts of the earlier Marks I, I* and III series rifles often bear unit or regimental markings, on the marking disc, or sometimes on the butt itself.

S.M.L.E. rifle serial numbers are usually found marked on the right side of the receiver ring, barrel knox form, rear flat of the bolt handle, nosecap boss, underside of the wooden fore-end near the nosecap, and underneath the backsight leaf. An inspection of these numbers can help to ascertain if these parts have been exchanged, in service or after government disposal. In service, such new replacement components were usually stamped with the rifle serial number. In some cases where numbered parts from other stripped rifles have been fitted by armourers, the original number will be found to have been barred out and the new serial number stamped alongside the original.

Drawings have been used in this section rather than photographs because of the more apparent detail in line drawings. In some cases, for example, the magazines, internal parts and positioning can be indicated too. Shadow, scale and projection angles can become a problem in some photographs and layouts when comparing parts, another reason for the use of line drawings. In the case of fore-ends illustrated on the following page, pointers have been used to identify the sometimes subtle differences.

S.M.L.E. magazine cases, floorplates and auxiliary springs are generally interchangeable in this series and are often found to be incorrectly fitted to some marks of S.M.L.E. rifles. Changes in magazines were mostly due to the introduction of new ammunition. Different round-nose and pointed projectiles could cause problems with correct staggered positioning of the rounds in the magazine should early ammunition be loaded into a later pattern magazine or *vice versa*. Problems could arise when feeding the cartridge into the chamber, due to the angle of departure from the magazine case when chambering a round. The riveted front lips on some magazines resulted in different shaped clearance recesses ground in the magazine cut-offs as well. The four different magazine cases, three platforms and four auxiliary springs have been fully described here to prevent any misunderstanding.

Four vertical text columns have been used in the six following pages, each applying to a certain rifle Mark or magazine type. While illustrations may disrupt these columns in some instances, column headers at the top of each page apply to the specific text columns for the whole page. The component part being described is named at the far left-hand side. Each illustration has been captioned in this section too, to avoid further confusion.

Rifle Model:	SMLE Mark I	SMLE Mark I*	SMLE Mark III	SMLE Mark III*
Fore-end:	Inner barrel band screw under outer band.	Inner barrel band screw under outer band.	Inner barrel band screw visible under fore-end.	Inner barrel band screw visible under fore-end.
	Provision for dial sight plate, LH side.	Provision for dial sight plate, LH side.	Provision for dial sight plate, LH side.	No provision for dial sight plate.
	No charger bridge slot.	No charger bridge slot.	Charger bridge slot.	Charger bridge slot.
	Provision for cut-off.	Provision for cut-off.	Provision for cut-off.	No provision for cut-off.
	Recess for long range aperture rearsight.	Recess for long range aperture rearsight.	Recess for long range aperture rearsight.	No recess for long range aperture rearsight.
	No provision for sight protector wings on fore-end.	No provision for sight protector wings on fore-end.	Provision for backsight protector wings.	Provision for backsight protector wings.

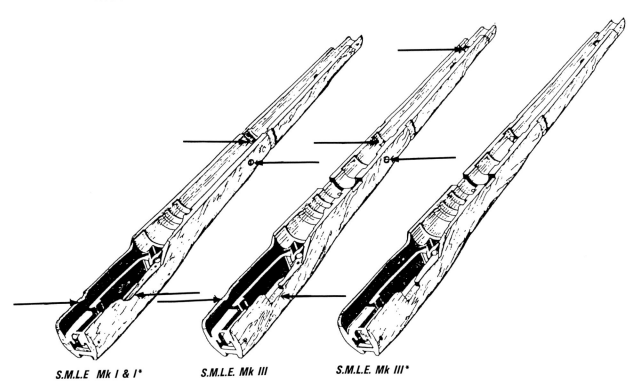

S.M.L.E Mk I & I*   S.M.L.E. Mk III   S.M.L.E. Mk III*

Handguards —				
front:	Square shoulder step-down at outer band.	Square shoulder step-down at outer band.	Rounded shoulder for outer band.	Rounded shoulder for outer band.
rear:	Steel sight protector wings inletted.	Steel sight protector wings inletted.	No attached sight protector wings.	No attached sight protector wings.
	Early model had only one set of spring clips.	Two sets of spring clips to fasten around barrel.	Two sets of spring clips to fasten around barrel.	Two sets of spring clips to fasten around barrel

S.M.L.E. Mk I & I*

S.M.L.E. Mk III & III*

Rifle Model:	**SMLE Mark I**	**SMLE Mark I***	**SMLE Mark III**	**SMLE Mark III***
Backsight:	Windage adjustment. Bone inserts on slide. Backsight bed mounts on top of barrel.	Windage adjustment. Bone inserts on slide. Backsight bed mounts on top of barrel.	Windage adjustment. All-steel slide. Backsight bed fits around the barrel.	No windage adjustment. All steel slide. Backsight bed fits around the barrel.

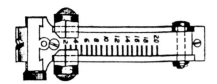

S.M.L.E. Mk I & I*

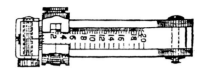

S.M.L.E. Mk III

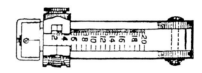

S.M.L.E. Mk III*

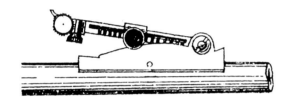

S.M.L.E. Mk I & I*

S.M.L.E. Mk III

Rifle Model:	**SMLE Mark I**	**SMLE Mark I***	**SMLE Mark III**	**SMLE Mk III***
Dial Sight:	Graduated 1,600 to 2,800 yds on the plate for Mk II ammunition; marked "L.E.S." In 1911, plates re-graduated for Mk VII, marked "L.E.S. 2".	Graduated 1,600 to 2,800 yds on the plate for Mk VI ammunition; marked "L.E.S." In 1911, plates re-graduated for Mk VII, marked "L.E.S. 2".	Graduated 1,600 to 2,800 yds on the plate for Mk VI ammunition; marked "L.E.S. III" In 1911, plates re-graduated for Mk VII, marked "L.E.S. 2".	No long-range aperture or dial sight plate and pointer fitted; no provision for plate or rear aperture in the fore-end either.

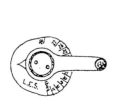

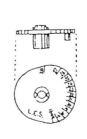

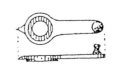

Long Range Dial Sight

Rifle Model:	SMLE Mark I	SMLE Mark I*	SMLE Mark III	SMLE Mark III*
Body & Bolt	Charger guides on left side of action body and on top of the bolthead. Angled stop/guide, at front of right wall in boltway, near the bolt retaining spring nib. Magazine cut-off slot.	Charger guides on left side of action body and on top of the bolthead. Angled stop/guide, at front of right wall in boltway, near the bolt retaining spring nib. Magazine cut-off slot.	Charger bridge mounted across top of action body, secured by rivets. No guide on bolthead. No stop on right side of boltway, to rear of the bolt retaining spring nib. Magazine cut-off slot.	Charger bridge mounted across top of action body, secured by rivets. No guide on bolthead. No stop on right side of boltway, to rear of the bolt retaining spring nib. No magazine cut-off slot.

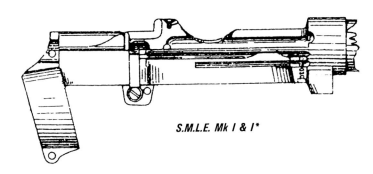

S.M.L.E. Mk I & I*

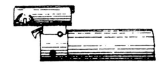

S.M.L.E. Mk I & I*

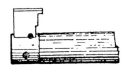

S.M.L.E. Mk III & III*

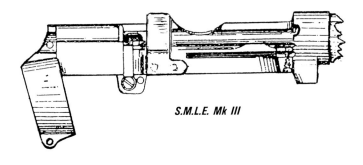

S.M.L.E. Mk III

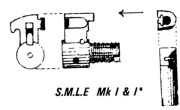

S.M.L.E Mk I & I*

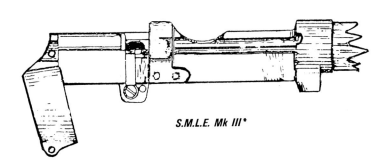

S.M.L.E. Mk III*

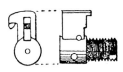

S.M.L.E. Mk III & III*

The .22-in. rimfire bolthead (right) has a two-piece firing pin. Its rear section is a shortened .303-in. striker cut off at the shoulder, so that the original tapered point is removed. The forward section is housed inside the bolthead, which is readily identified by its off-centre firing pin hole for the rimfire cartridge. Such boltheads are often found marked ".22 No. 2".

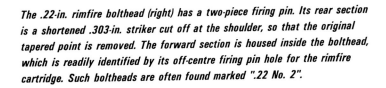

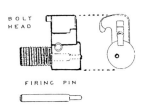

.22 No. 2 Bolthead and front striker.

Rifle Model:	**SMLE Mark I**	**SMLE Mark I***	**SMLE Mark III**	**SMLE Mk III***
Nosecap:	Incurving nosecap sight protector ears.	Incurving nosecap sight protector ears.	Parallel nosecap sight protector ears.	Parallel nosecap sight protector ears. In Australian service, some had "windows" cut into protector wings, for easier foresight adjustment.

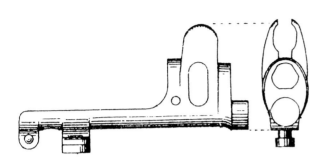

S.M.L.E. Mk I & I*

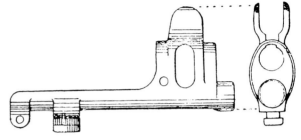

S.M.L.E. Mk III & III*

Rifle Model:	**SMLE Mark I**	**SMLE Mark I***	**SMLE Mark III**	**SMLE Mk III***
Buttplate:	Sheet steel. No provision for trap.	Gunmetal, like brass. Has butt trap.	Gunmetal, like brass. Has butt trap.	Gunmetal, like brass. Has butt trap.

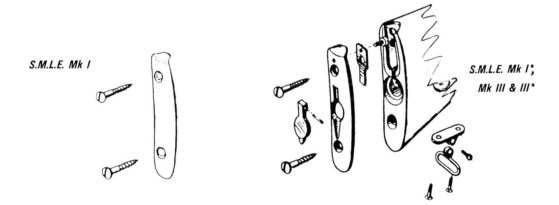

S.M.L.E. Mk I

S.M.L.E. Mk I*, Mk III & III*

Rifle Model:	**SMLE Mark I**	**SMLE Mark I***	**SMLE Mark III**	**SMLE Mk III***
Swivels:	Butt swivel attached to square woodscrew.	Butt swivel mounts on inletted fixture.	Butt swivel mounts on inletted fixture.	Butt swivel mounts on inletted fixture.

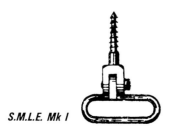

S.M.L.E. Mk I

S.M.L.E. Mk I*, Mk III & III*

Introduced with the new Short Rifle, the No. 1 magazine is about ⅛-in. deeper than that for the M.L.E. Rifle.

A magazine stop clip is riveted at the front right side of the magazine case. This serves to keep the bullet of the top cartridge in the right hand column in proper position for feed into the chamber.

A fixed lip is on the left side of the case.

A staple loop and link attach the magazine to the trigger guard.

The No. 1 magazine was intended for use with .303 Mark VI cartridges.

This magazine case was introduced with the Mark I* S.M.L.E. and is deeper at the front end to facilitate loading.

The No. 2 has a similar magazine stop clip riveted onto the front right hand side of the case. This can be pivoted forwards in order to remove the magazine floorplate and spring from the magazine case.

A fixed lip is on the left side of the case.

The magazine link loop was deleted, §13509, from late 1905.

The No. 2 magazine was intended for use with .303 Mark VI cartridges.

Introduced for the new Mark VII pointed nose ammunition, many of the No. 1 and No. 2 cases were converted. The No. 3 case is a conversion of the Nos. 1 or 2 case, with spring lip riveted on the left side.

A flat spring has also been fitted onto the rib at the back of the magazine case. The back rib is stamped "3". The lip on the left side is a spring type.

No magazine link loop was fitted. Converted cases had this cut off.

The No. 3 magazine was intended for use with .303 Mark VI and Mk VII cartridges.

The new No. 4 case has fixed lips, instead of riveted types. All the No. 4 cases were newly made, not converted.

No magazine stop clip was required because the lip was an integral part of the case.

Vertical rib on the back of the case incorporates a small flat spring, the same as the No. 3 case. The back rib is stamped with the number "4".

The lips on No. 4 cases are integral types. These new-made cases had no requirement for the link loop.

The No. 4 magazine was intended for use with .303 Mark VI and Mk VII cartridges.

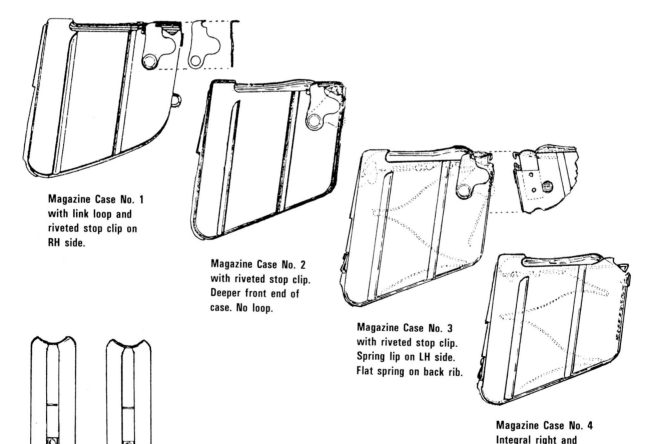

Magazine Case No. 1 with link loop and riveted stop clip on RH side.

Magazine Case No. 2 with riveted stop clip. Deeper front end of case. No loop.

Magazine Case No. 3 with riveted stop clip. Spring lip on LH side. Flat spring on back rib.

Magazine Case No. 4 Integral right and left side lips. Flat spring on back rib.

Typical case no. designations found stamped on the lower part of the case back rib, just underneath the flat spring.

The magazine platform is raised on the left side, to stagger the cartridges in order. A zig-zag spring acts on the magazine platform. The previous M.L.E. magazine has a C-shaped spring.

The magazine platform was the same as that used in the No. 1 magazine case. The flat zig-zag spring is identical with that on the No. 1 magazine for the S.M.L.E. Mk 1 rifle.

Uses a "No. 2" platform, reduced at the left side. Stamped "2" on top of platform. A flat ribbon zig-zag spring is used to keep the magazine platform and cartridges in position against the lips.

"No. 3" platform has no bottom plate underneath and a narrower front end. Stamped "3". Like the previous Nos. 1, 2 & 3 cases with Nos. 1 & 2 platforms, a flat ribbon zig-zag spring is utilised.

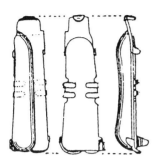

Platform No. 1, for Nos. 1 & 2 magazines.

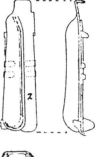

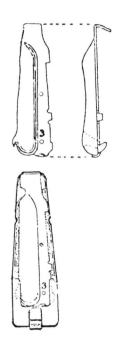

M.L.E. "C" spring (left). Compare this with the zig-zag spring of the S.M.L.E. magazine at right.

Platform No. 2, for No. 3 magazine.

Platform No. 3, for No. 4 magazine.

An auxiliary magazine spring with curved end was fitted at the front to keep this end of the platform at the correct angle, when the magazine was loaded with cartridges.

A No. 2 auxiliary spring with straight (instead of curved) end was used in the No. 2 magazine. This new spring was stamped "2", as was the back of the magazine case.

The No. 3 auxiliary spring was a re-set No. 1 or No. 2 spring and it was stamped "3". These conversions can usually be readily identified by these markings.

The new flat auxiliary spring which fits down the front of the magazine case is stamped with the figure "4". The No. 4 auxiliary springs were all of new manufacture.

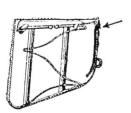

Auxiliary spring on Magazine No. 1.

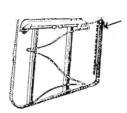

Auxiliary spring on Magazine No. 2.

Auxiliary spring on Magazine No. 3.

Auxiliary spring on Magazine No. 4.

SPECIFICATIONS

RIFLE, SHORT LEE-ENFIELD, .303, Marks III & III*

Lengths:
Rifle, overall	3 ft. 8.5 in. [1130mm] *with normal butt*
With bayonet fixed	5 ft. 2 in. [1575mm] *approximate*
Barrel	25.2 in. [640mm]
Bayonet, overall	1 ft. 9.75 in. [552mm] *Pattern 1907*
Bayonet, blade	1 ft. 5.0 in. [432mm]

Weights:
Rifle, Mk III	8 lb. 10.5 oz. [3.9 kg] *with empty magazine*
Rifle, Mk III*	8 lb. 15 oz. [4.1 kg] *with empty magazine*
Sword bayonet	1 lb. 0.5 oz. [.47 kg] *without scabbard*

Barrel:
Rifling	5 groove, Enfield
Rifling twist	L.H., 1 turn in 10 ins. or 33 calibres
Groove depth at muzzle ...	.0065 in.
Groove depth at breech ...	.00575 in.
Width of lands	.0936 in.

Sights: ... ...
Leaf backsight, 200 — 2,000 yds.
Blade foresight
Sighting radius, 1 ft. 7 in (19 in.)
Dial sight, 1,600 — 2,800 yds. *Mk III*

Method of Operation ... ... Manually operated bolt, locking lugs at rear
Method of Loading ... ... 5-round charger clips

Cartridge ... ... .303-in. British
Muzzle Velocity, Mk VI ball ... 2,060 ft./sec. *approximate*
Mk VII ball ... 2,440 ft./sec. *approximate*

Production Costs: ... ...
£4/11/4½d (Mk I, 1904) *Enfield, England*
£3/4/2¼d (Mk I*, 1906) *Enfield, England*
£4/1/6d (Mk III, 1913) *Lithgow, Australia*
£3/15/0d (Mk III, 1914) *B.S.A. or L.S.A., England*
£7/10/0d (Mk III*, 1941) *Lithgow, Australia*
£9/10/0d (Mk III*, 1943) *B.S.A., England*

Service Accessories: ... ...
Pattern 1907 Bayonet & Scabbard
Webbing sling
Oil bottle
Pullthrough & Flannel

COCKED . . .

LOWER RIB OF TRIGGER IN CONTACT WITH THE SEAR. FULL BENT OF COCKING PIECE HELD ON NOSE OF SEAR. MAINSPRING COMPRESSED.

Two-stage trigger pull . . .
lower rib on the trigger engages
on first pull, second pull occurs
as the upper rib engages the sear.

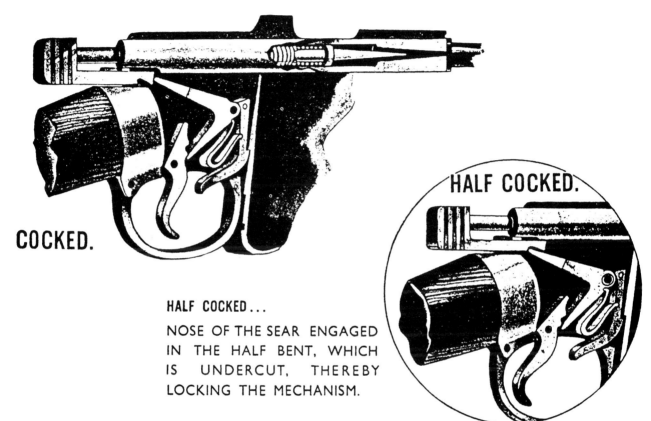

COCKED.

HALF COCKED.

HALF COCKED . . .

NOSE OF THE SEAR ENGAGED IN THE HALF BENT, WHICH IS UNDERCUT, THEREBY LOCKING THE MECHANISM.

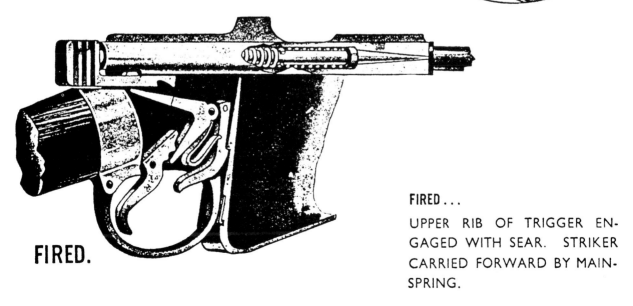

FIRED.

FIRED . . .

UPPER RIB OF TRIGGER ENGAGED WITH SEAR. STRIKER CARRIED FORWARD BY MAINSPRING.

USER GUIDE

for PARTS and VOCAB. LISTS

IMPORTANT— Read this section first.

The Identification Lists published here utilise military service equipment catalogue and part list references. While the original wartime lists have been edited and updated in some parts, the original nomenclature and format has, by necessity, been retained. This *User Guide* section should be studied in order to better understand the original listings and descriptions, their arrangement, and thus how to best use them.

The *REF. NO.* is the reference number to the specific parts illustrated and labelled with the corresponding number on the adjacent page. The *DESIGNATION* is the original service part name. For this tabulated description, lines have been indented where that particular line applies to the previous line. For example, in British service parlance, the Washer, spring, screw, band inner, barrel assembly for the Rifle, No. 1 Mk III .303-in., (shown on page 17 and illustrated as Part No. 5) is part of the Inner band group for the Barrel assembly.

e.g.	BARREL ASSEMBLY	*Part assembly group.*
	BARREL	*Part group, applicable to Barrel Assembly.*
	BAND, inner	*Part group, applies to Barrel Assembly rather than Barrel.*
	SCREW	*Component part for the Inner band.*
	SPRING	*Component part for the Screw.*
	WASHER	*Component part for the Spring.*

Where the following line is indented, that particular item is part of, or related to, the preceding line, and so on, virtually *ad infinitum.*

VOCAB. NUMBER is the service part number; these were usually printed or written on the original packaging or attached labels, essentially for stores reference. Comprising of letter prefixes to numbers, this prefix was also a service indicator. Original British stores numbers use two letters, where a third letter "A" is added, this has been a special Australian modification. Relative part nomenclature will often have the suffix (Aust.) as well, to indicate peculiarity to Australian production. An example is the copper recoil plates in the fore-end, found only in Australian manufacture because the Australian Coachwood or Queensland Maple timber was softer than European Walnut used in British production. These copper blocks are part no. BAA 3410. Another example here is the "cap, backsight, (Aust)" and its related parts, which also differ from their British counterparts.

Regarding the British Vocab. No. prefixes, these appear to have commenced with "AA" during the earlier .303 S.M.L.E. era. "BA 0xxx" and "BB 0xxx" are applied to the No. 1 rifle here, "AA" is an earlier prefix applied to the rifle sling. "BB 0xxx" was also used for the .303 No. 3 Mark I* (T) or Pattern 1914 Sniper rifle, while "BB 8xxx" is used for the No. 4 rifle of similar vintage. "BB" applied to the No. 4 Mk I while "BJ" generally relates to the Mk I* variant. These were also used with the Rifle No. 5 parts, where applicable. "CR" parts number prefixes for the No. 4 series seem to date from around 1950, post-war, and continued into the 7.62mm NATO era.

Continuing this sequence, "BD" prefixes were applied to the .303 Vickers Machine Gun, "BE" to the 9mm Sten Machine Carbine and also for the .303 Bren Light Machine Gun. "CAA" was applied to Australia's 9mm Owen and Austen Machine Carbines; again note the additional "A" at the end, for specific Australian stores. Of course, some exceptions may be found among these Vocab. No. letter prefixes when one dares to generalise, but there will usually be an appropriate reason. However, the Vocab No. prefixes can be good indicators and also provide a better overall understanding of the ordnance service stores and parts system.

Vocab. Nos. with an unusual combination prefix such as G1/GAA. 5852 (wing nut for the 2½-in. grenade discharger) indicate extra-service supply. G1/GAA 5852 with the extra "A" suffix also denotes a part special to Australian supply and ordnance. "G1/GA" indicated commercially available articles such as ironmongery and hardware items. Some washers, screws, nuts and bolts which were readily available from commercial sources were included in this particular category. But even where such common items were manufactured at ordnance factories, the usual service parts numbers and designations were still applied.

The asterisk (*) often seen in the Designation column indicates that these particular component parts were available through the ordnance supply system for Workshop replacement. In Australian service this was performed by the A.E.M.E. (Australian Electrical and Mechanical Engineers) while its British service counterpart was the E.M.E. (Electrical and Mechanical Engineers). These, and other such abbreviations will sometimes be encountered in instructions. A table of the principal abbreviations is provided at the bottom of this page.

Major component groups do not have the Reference Number or Vocabulary Number in the appropriate column. In these cases, the particular entries have been left blank or marked with dot leaders. In this Vocabulary Number column, the abbreviation "GA" indicates a General Arrangement and an "A" signifies "Assembly", hence the absence of any part or vocab. numbers as these were assembly groups or sub-groups.

The *MAT.* column details the material, a further sub-description of the particular part. *NO. OFF* is the number of, or the quantity required for assembly and fitting. *DRAWING NUMBER* refers to the original manufacturer's part drawing. An A.D.D.(S) prefix to the drawing number indicates Australian origin (possibly Australian Design Department, Sydney?), D.D.(E) is an Enfield drawing (Design Department, Enfield), and S.A.I.D. and A.I.D. are also of British departmental origin.

The original M.G.O. parts drawings have been revised and new lay-outs applied in instances where the originals have been indistinct, or they have contained parts relevant to other, revised sections. And in some instances, minor component parts have been re-drawn.

The military and service Identification Lists referenced here were not initiated until World War 2, by which time the No. 1 S.M.L.E. rifle was no longer a front line issue in the European theatres. So the M.G.O. (Master-General of the Ordnance) and A.M.F. (Australian Military Forces) lists have been the prime source for parts lists and the original illustrations.

Abbreviations:

A.	Assembly	M.A.	Main Assembly
Aust.	Australian Pattern	Mk	Mark
B.A.	British Association	M.C.	Machine Carbine
B.S.F.	British Standard Fine	No.	Number
B.S.W.	British Standard Whitworth	N.P.	New Pattern
G.A.	General Arrangement	S.A.	Sub-Assembly
G.O.'s	General Orders	S.W.G.	Standard Wire Gauge
Inst.	Instrument	Vocab.	Vocabulary

Key Plate

RIFLE No1 S.M.L.E. .303 MK.III
(*With Cut-Off*)

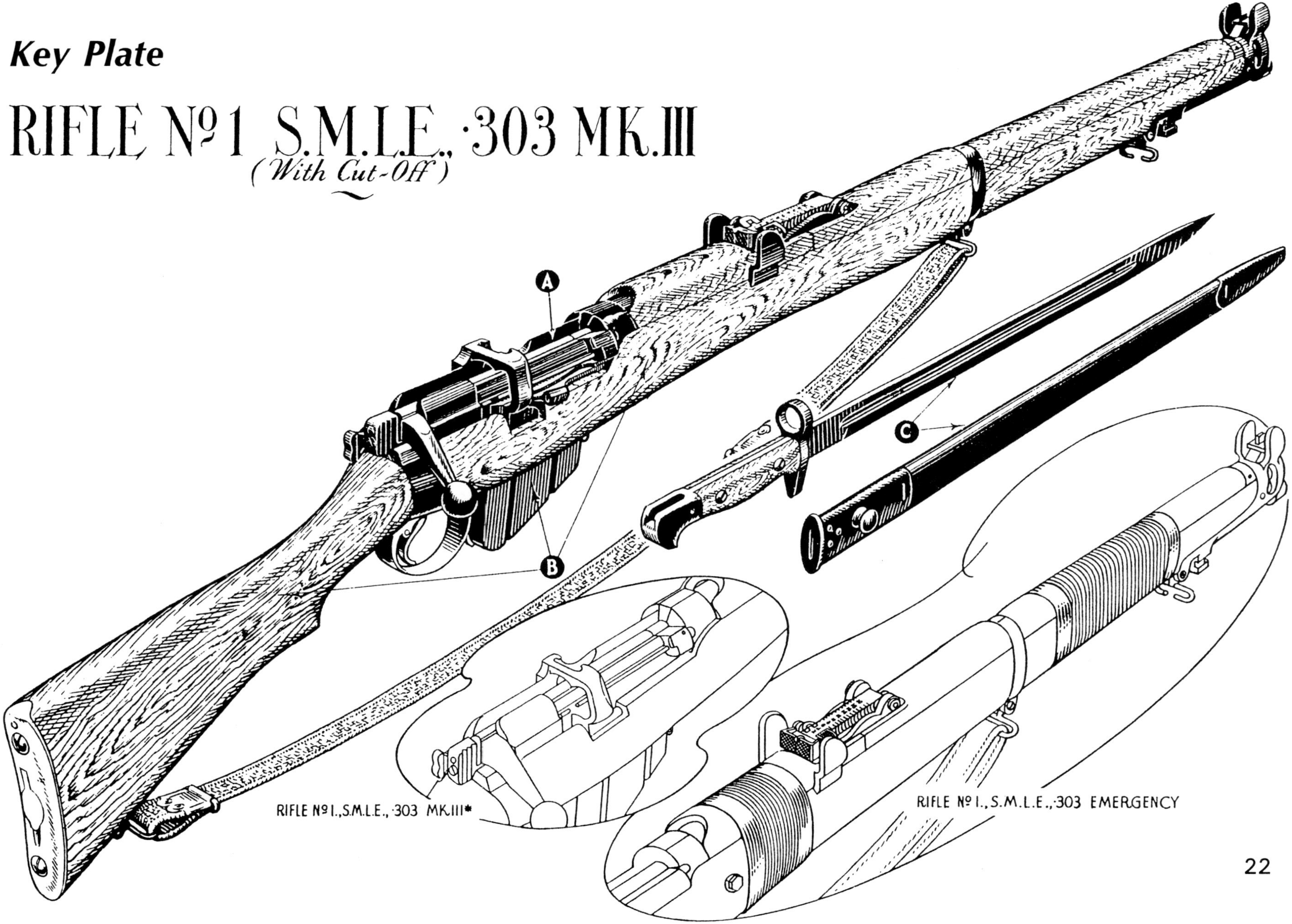

RIFLE No1, S.M.L.E., .303 EMERGENCY

RIFLE No1, S.M.L.E., .303 MK.III*

22

PLATES:—

REMARKS

RIFLE, No. 1 Mk III, S.M.L.E., .303-in. (with cut-off)

			REMARKS
With BANTAM BUTT	Vocab No. —	BA 0576 ...	1-in. shorter than the normal butt.
With LONG BUTT	Vocab No. —	BA 0577 ...	½-in. longer than the normal butt.
With NORMAL BUTT	Vocab No. —	BA 0578 ...	Not marked with "L", "S" or "B" stamp.
With SHORT BUTT	Vocab No. —	BA 0579 ...	½-in. shorter than the normal butt.
BARREL, WITH BODY	Vocab No. —	BB 0580	
(With Sights, assembled ["O" blade]; inner band; and pin, stop, bolt locking, 2)			
BODY	Vocab No. —	BB 0581	
(With Pin, stop, bolt locking, 2)			
CUT-OFF	Vocab No. —	BB 0582	
CUT-OFF SCREW	Vocab No. —	BB 0583	

RIFLE, No. 1 Mk III*, S.M.L.E., .303-in. (without cut-off)

			REMARKS
With BANTAM BUTT	Vocab No. —	BA 0590 ...	1-in. shorter than the normal butt.
With LONG BUTT	Vocab No. —	BA 0591 ...	½-in. longer than the normal butt.
With NORMAL BUTT	Vocab No. —	BA 0592 ...	Not marked with "L", "S" or "B" stamp.
With SHORT BUTT	Vocab No. —	BA 0593 ...	½-in. shorter than the normal butt.
BARREL, WITH BODY	Vocab No. —	BB 0594	
(With Sights, assembled ["O" blade]; inner band; and pin, stop, bolt locking, 2)			
BODY	Vocab No. —	BB 0595	
(With Pin, stop, bolt locking, 2)			

RIFLE, No. 1 Mk III*, S.M.L.E., .303-in. EMERGENCY (for Rifle Grenade Training)

(With wire binding around stock fore-end and hand guard; and screw, reinforcing, stock, fore-end).

	Vocab No. —	BC 0642

All components (with the exception of those listed above) of RIFLE, No. 1 Mk III* and Rifle, No. 1 Mk III, EMERGENCY, same as RIFLE, No. 1 Mk III.

Plate A₁

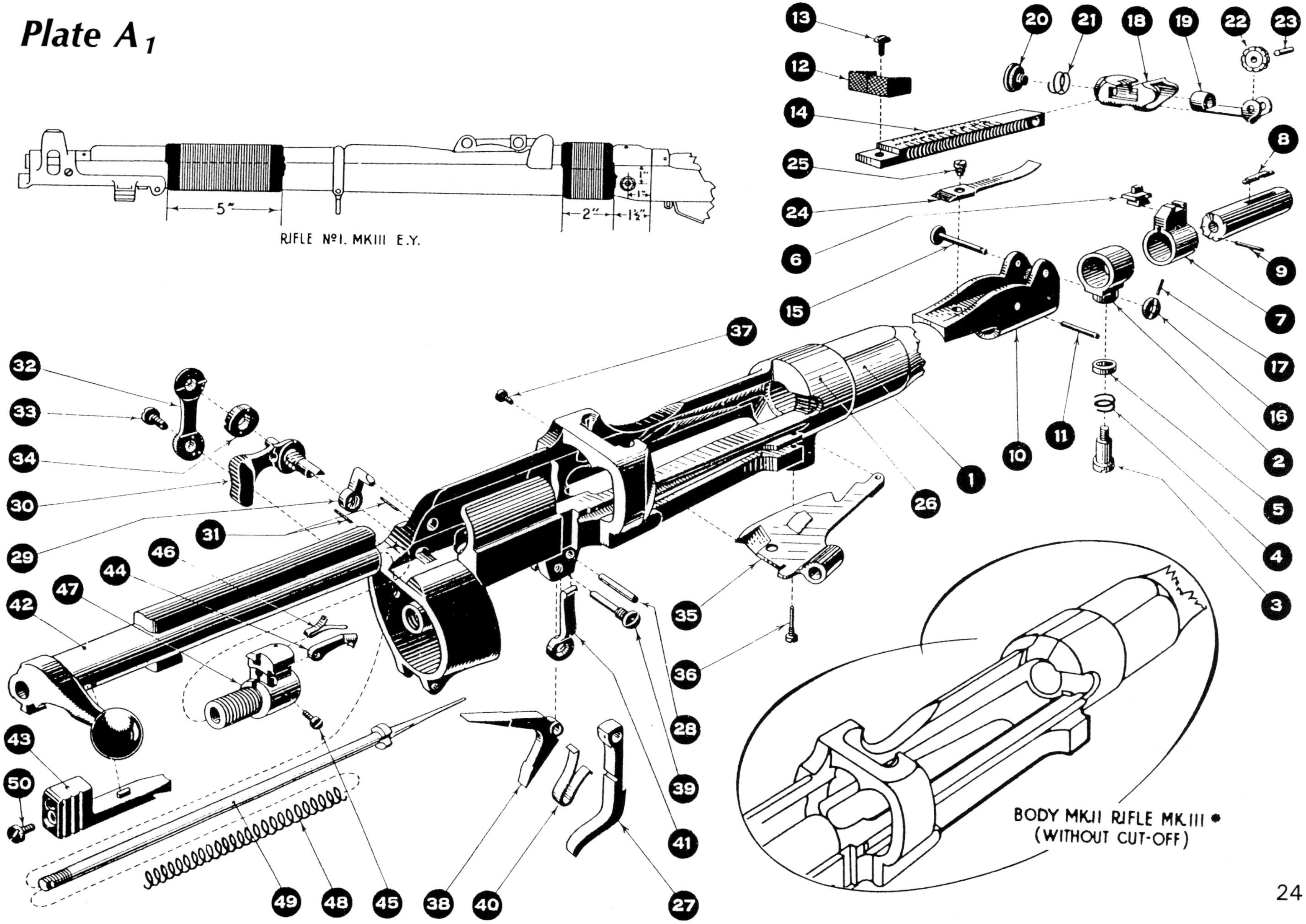

BODY MKII RIFLE MKIII *
(WITHOUT CUT-OFF)

RIFLE Nº I. MKIII E.Y.

2″

1½″

5″

REF. NO.	DESIGNATION	VOCAB. NUMBER	MAT.	NO. OFF	DRAWING NUMBER	REMARKS
Plate A1						
...	RIFLE, No. 1 Mk III, .303-in.	General Arrangement				
...	BARREL ASSEMBLY	Assembly				
A 1	BARREL (a)	...	Steel	1	SAID 1317	Sometimes made of brass.
2	BAND, inner	...	Steel	1	SAID 1318	
3	SCREW	* BB 0724	Steel	1	SAID 1318	
4	SPRING	* BB 0757	Spring Steel	1	SAID 1320	
5	WASHER	* BB 0783	Steel	1	SAID 1319	
...	FORESIGHT	Sub-Assembly				
6	BLADE	* ...	Steel	1	SAID 1320	Blackened.
	Sizes— -.06"	* BB 0654			SAID 1318	
	-.045"	* BB 0655			SAID 1318	
	-.03"	* BB 0656			SAID 1318	
	-.015"	* BB 0657			SAID 1318	
	"0"	* BB 0658			SAID 1318	
	+.015"	* BB 0659			SAID 1318	
	+.03"	* BB 0660			SAID 1318	
	+.045"	* BB 6145			SAID 1318	
7	BLOCK, band	* BAA 3403	Steel	1	SAID 1318	
8	KEY	* BAA 3405	Steel	1	SAID 1318	
9	PIN, fixing	* BAA 3408	Steel	1	SAID 1320	

(a) Barrel, without body, with sights * BAA 3400

* Indicates component part available for Workshop replacement.

N.B.:— Dissimilarities to the British production may be noted in component parts with the "BAA" Vocabulary No. prefix.

Plate A₂

Plate A2

RIFLE, No. 1 Mk III, .303-in. (continued)

BARREL ASSEMBLY (continued)

REF. NO.	DESIGNATION		VOCAB. NUMBER	MAT.	NO. OFF	DRAWING NUMBER	REMARKS
...	BACKSIGHT		Sub-Assembly				
A 10	BED	*	BAA 3401	Steel	1	SAID 1318	
11	PIN, fixing	*	BAA 3407	Steel	1	SAID 1320	
12	CAP (b)	*	BB 0665	Steel	1	SAID 1318	Mk III rifle had windage adjustment on the back-sight cap.
13	SCREW (c)	*	BB 0726	Steel	1	SAID 1320	
14	LEAF, "B" (d)	*	BB 0696	Steel	1	SAID 1318	
15	PIN, axis	*	BB 0706	Steel	1	SAID 1320	
16	WASHER	*	BB 0781	Steel	1	SAID 1320	
17	PIN	*	BB 0716	Steel	1	SAID 1320	
18	SLIDE	*	BB 0747	Steel	1	SAID 1318	
19	CATCH	*	BB 0672	Steel	1	SAID 1318	
20	SCREW	*	BB 0730	Steel	1	SAID 1320	
21	SPRING	*	BB 0751	Spring Steel	1	SAID 1319	
22	WORM	*	BB 0786	Steel	1	SAID 1318	
23	PIN	*	BB 0717	Steel	1	SAID 1320	
24	SPRING, sight back	*	BB 0760	Spring Steel	1	SAID 1319	
25	SCREW	*	BB 0741	Steel	1	SAID 1320	
(b)	Cap, backsight, (Aust)	*	BAA 3404	Steel			Later type of leaf and cap.
(c)	Screw, cap, backsight (Aust)	*	BAA 3413	Steel			Front of cap tapers to leaf rather than a square front.
(d)	Leaf, backsight, (Aust)	*	BAA 3406	Steel			

Note: (b), (c) and (d) are used on Rifles manufactured since 1943.

*   Indicates component part available for Workshop replacement.

N.B.:— Dissimilarities to the British production may be noted in component parts with the "BAA" Vocabulary No. prefix.

Plate A₃

Plate A3

RIFLE, No. 1 Mk III, .303-in. (continued)
BODY ASSEMBLY
Assembly

REF. NO.	DESIGNATION		VOCAB. NUMBER	MAT.	NO. OFF	DRAWING NUMBER	REMARKS
A 26	BODY . . .		BB 0595	Steel	1	SAID 1318	Mk III* body, no mag cut-off.
27	CATCH, magazine .	*	BB 0670	Steel	1	SAID 1318	
28	PIN . .	*	BB 0707	Steel	1	SAID 1320	
29	CATCH, safety .	*	BB 0671	Steel	1	SAID 1318	
30	BOLT, locking .	*	BB 0662	Steel	1	SAID 1318	
31	PIN, stop .	*	BB 0713	Steel	2	SAID 1320	
32	SPRING, Mk I (e)	*	BB 0750	Steel	1	SAID 1319	Mk II spring is plain flat type.
33	SCREW, Mk I (f)	*	BB 0740	Steel	1	SAID 1320	
34	WASHER, Mk I (g)	*	BB 0784	Steel	1	SAID 1320	
35	CUT-OFF .		. . .	Steel	1	. . .	No provision on Mk III* rifle
36	SCREW .		. . .	Steel	1	. . .	for magazine cut-off.
37	SCREW, ejector, "B"	*	BB 0733	Steel	1	SAID 1320	
38	SEAR . .	*	BB 0746	Steel	1	SAID 1318	
39	SCREW . .	*	BB 0739	Steel	1	SAID 1320	
40	SPRING . .	*	BB 0759	Spring Steel	1	SAID 1319	
41	SPRING, retaining .	*	BB 0756	Spring Steel	1	SAID 1319	

(e) Also Spring, Mk II.   *   BB 7931
(f) Also Screw, Mk II.
     To be demanded as Screw, cap,
     backsight (Cat. No. BB 0726)   *
(g) Also Washer, Mk II.   *   BAA 7931

Note: (e), (f) and (g) are used on Rifles manufactured since 1943.

*   Indicates component part available for Workshop replacement.

N.B.:— Dissimilarities to the British production may be noted in component parts with the "BAA" Vocabulary No. prefix.

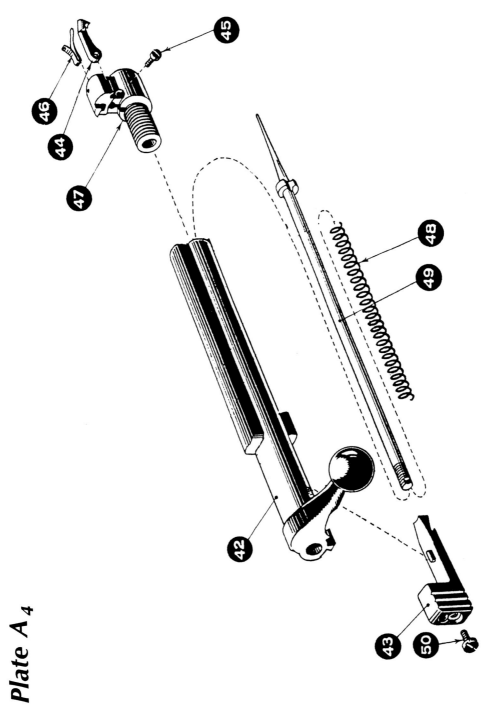

Plate A₄

Plate A4

RIFLE, No. 1 Mk III, .303-in. (continued)
BOLT, BREECH ASSEMBLY Sub-Assembly

REF. NO.	DESIGNATION		VOCAB. NUMBER	MAT.	NO. OFF	DRAWING NUMBER	REMARKS
A 42	BOLT	*	BB 0661	Steel	1	SAID 1318	
43	COCKING PIECE, "B" .	*	BB 0675	Steel	1	SAID 1318	Early cocking piece had
44	EXTRACTOR .	*	BB 0680	Steel	1	SAID 1318	knurled button end.
45	SCREW . . .	*	BB 0734	Steel	1	SAID 1320	
46	SPRING . .	*	BB 0752	Spring Steel	1	SAID 1319	
47	HEAD . . .	*	BB 0690	Steel	1	SAID 1318	
48	SPRING, main . .	*	BB 0754	Spring Steel	1	SAID 1319	
49	STRIKER, "B" . .	*	BB 0769	Steel	1	SAID 1318	
50	SCREW . .	*	BB 0741	Steel	1	SAID 1320	

* Indicates component part available for Workshop replacement.

As illustrated in S.A.I.S. #19 *Australian S.M.L.E. Variations*, differences will be found in the machining and form of cocking pieces, nosecaps, trigger guards, piling swivels, rearsight protectors, inner and outer bands, rearsights, &c. as production proceeded. Minor differences may also be noted between the Enfield R.S.A.F., B.S.A. Co., L.S.A. Co., S.S.A. & N.R.F. Peddled Scheme, Lithgow and Ishapore rifles component parts.

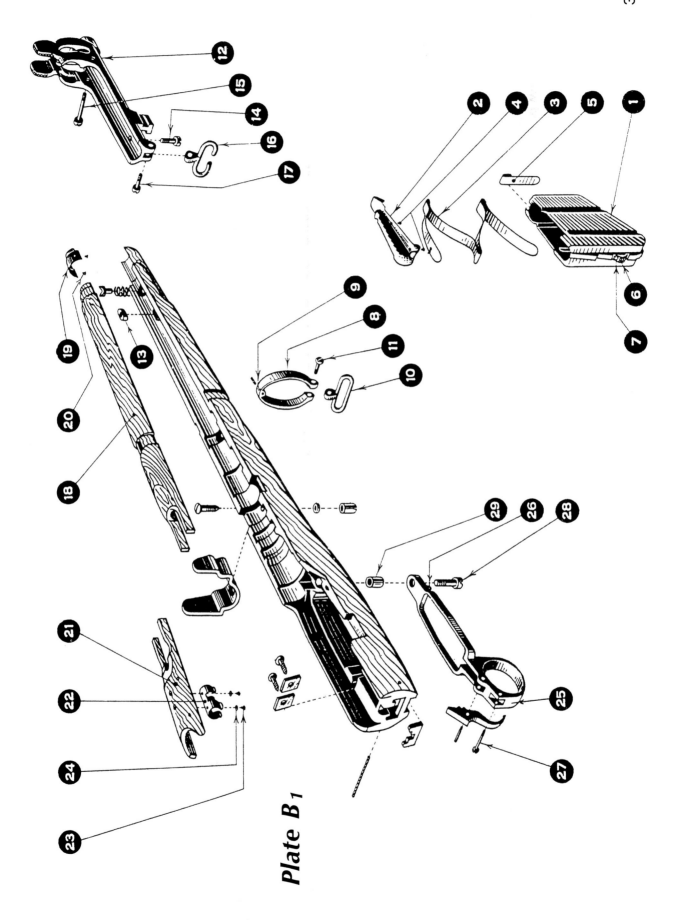

Plate B₁

Plate B1

RIFLE, No. 1 Mk III, .303-in. (continued)

REF. NO.	DESIGNATION		VOCAB. NUMBER	MAT.	NO. OFF	DRAWING NUMBER	REMARKS
...	**MAGAZINE "B"**	*	BB 0698 SA				Earlier Mk III rifles were fitted with the No. 3 type magazine case with No. 2 platform.
B 1	CASE, "B"	*	BB 0669	Steel	1	SAID 1317	
2	PLATFORM, "B"	*	BB 0721	Steel	1	SAID 1317	
3	SPRING	*	. . .	Spring Steel	1	SAID 1319	
4	RIVET	*	BAA 3411	Mild Steel	2	SAID 1320	
5	SPRING, auxiliary, "B"	*	BB 0749	Spring Steel	1	SAID 1319	
6	SPRING, rib	*	BAA 3414	Spring Steel	1	SAID 1319	
7	RIVET	*	BAA 3412	Mild Steel	1	SAID 1320	
...	**STOCK ASSEMBLY**	*	BB 0652			SAID 1317	
8	BAND, outer	*	BAA 3409	Steel	1	SAID 1318	Some Australian production bands made from brass.
9	PIN, joint	*	BB 0774	Steel	1	SAID 1320	
10	SWIVEL, sling	*	BB 0744	Steel	1	SAID 1319	
11	SCREW	*	BB 0667	Steel	1	SAID 1320	
12	CAP, nose	*	BB 0700	Steel	1	SAID 1318	
13	NUT	*	BB 0728	Steel	1	SAID 1320	
14	SCREW, back	*	BB 0729	Steel	1	SAID 1320	
15	SCREW, front	*	BB 0773	Steel	1	SAID 1320	
16	SWIVEL, piling, "B"		BB 0744	Steel	1	SAID 1319	Later pattern had no screw thread for a piling swivel.
17	SCREW	*	BB 0685	Steel	1	SAID 1320	No piling swivel or screw on later production.
18	GUARD, hand, front	*	BB 0666	Wood	1	SAID 1317	
19	CAP	*	BB 0727	Steel	1	SAID 1317	
20	SCREW	*	BB 0686	Steel	2	SAID 1320	
21	GUARD, hand, rear	*	BB 0753	Wood	1	SAID 1317	
22	SPRING	*	BB 0723	Spring Steel	1	SAID 1319	
23	RIVET	*	BB 0779	Copper	2	SAID 1320	
24	WASHER	*	BB 0687	Copper	2	SAID 1320	
25	GUARD, trigger	*	. . .	Steel	1	SAID 1318	Early trigger guards were relieved for No. 3 magazine case with the riveted lip.
26	LOOP, cover, breech		BB 0735	Steel	1	SAID 1318	
27	SCREW, back	*	BB 0736	Steel	1	SAID 1320	
28	SCREW, front	*	BB 0676	Steel	1	SAID 1320	
29	COLLAR	*		Steel	1	SAID 1319	

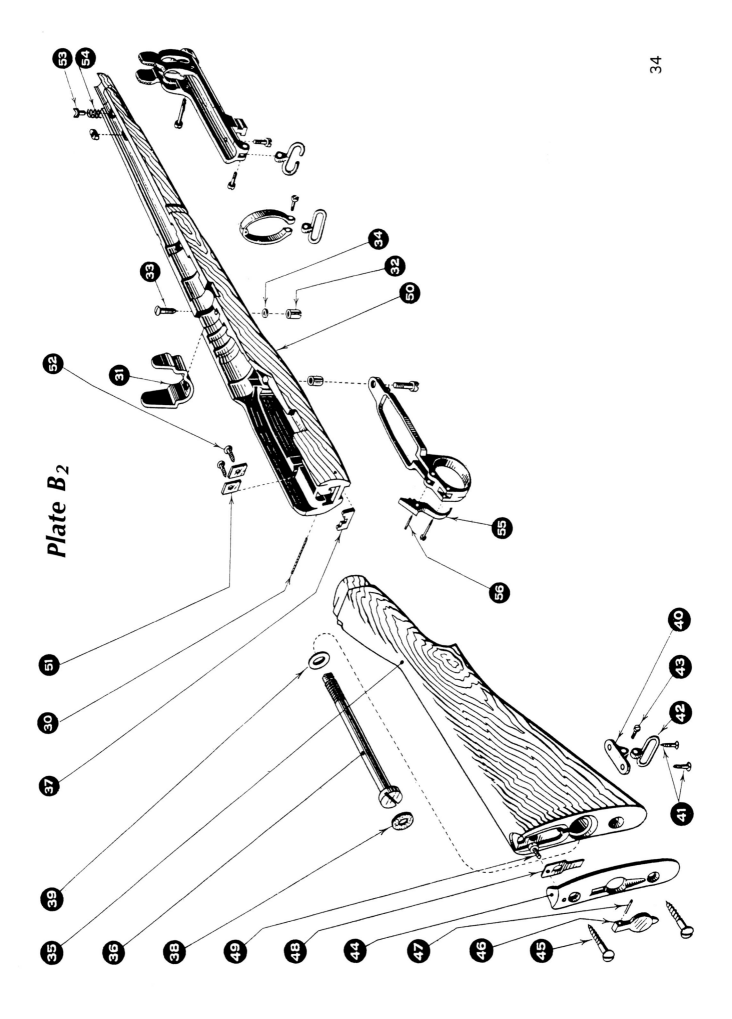

Plate B₂

Plate B2

RIFLE, No. 1 Mk III, .303-in. (continued)
STOCK ASSEMBLY (continued)

REF. NO.	DESIGNATION	VOCAB. NUMBER	MAT.	NO. OFF	DRAWING NUMBER	REMARKS
. . .						
B 30	PIN, screwed, fore-end.	. .	Brass	1	SAID 1320	
31	PROTECTOR . .	* BB 0722	Steel	1	SAID 1317	Early style had recesses
32	NUT . . .	* BB 0701	Steel	1	SAID 1320	milled into side wings.
33	SCREW . .	* BB 0738	Steel	1	SAID 1320	
34	WASHER, nut, screw.	* BB 0780	Steel	1	SAID 1320	
35	STOCK, butt, Mk I. ¶	. .	Wood		SAID 1317	¶ STOCK, butt, sizes:—
36	BOLT, "A" .	* BB 0663	Steel	1	SAID 1319	* Bantam BB 9764
37	PLATE . .	* BB 0719	Steel	1	SAID 1319	* Long BB 0765
38	WAD . .	* BB 0777	Leather	1	SAID 1320	* Normal BB 0766
39	WASHER .	* BB 0778	Steel	1	SAID 1320	* Short BB 0767
40	BRACKET .	* BB 0664	Steel	1	SAID 1318	Early butt had marking disc.
41	SCREW . .	* BB 0725	Steel	2	SAID 1320	
42	SWIVEL, sling .	* BB 0774	Steel	1	SAID 1319	
43	SCREW . .	BB 0744	Steel	1	SAID 1320	
44	PLATE, butt (h)	* . .	Brass	1	SAID 1319	
45	SCREW . .	* BB 0737	Steel	2	SAID 1320	
46	TRAP . .	* BB 0775	Brass	1	SAID 1318	
47	PIN . .	* BB 0714	Steel	1	SAID 1320	
48	SPRING . .	* BB 0762	Spring Steel	1	SAID 1319	
49	SCREW . .	* BB 0742	Steel	1	SAID 1320	
50	STOCK, fore-end 'B'	* BB 0768	Wood	1	SAID 1317	Mk III fore-end had dial
51	PLATE, copper (i)	* BAA 3410	Copper	2	*not on*	sight provision.
52	SCREW . .	. .	Brass	2	*British made*	
53	STUD . .	* BB 0771	Steel	1	SAID 1317	
54	SPRING . .	* BB 0761	Spring Steel	1	SAID 1319	
55	TRIGGER . .	* BB 0776	Steel	1	SAID 1318	
56	PIN . .	* BB 0715	Steel	1	SAID 1320	

(h) Plate, butt, Assembled * BB 0718
(i) Includes screws
* Indicates component part available for Workshop replacement.

¶ Normal butt at 12.5 in. long, ½-inch differences in lengths. Measured with buttplate fitted, distance to action body.

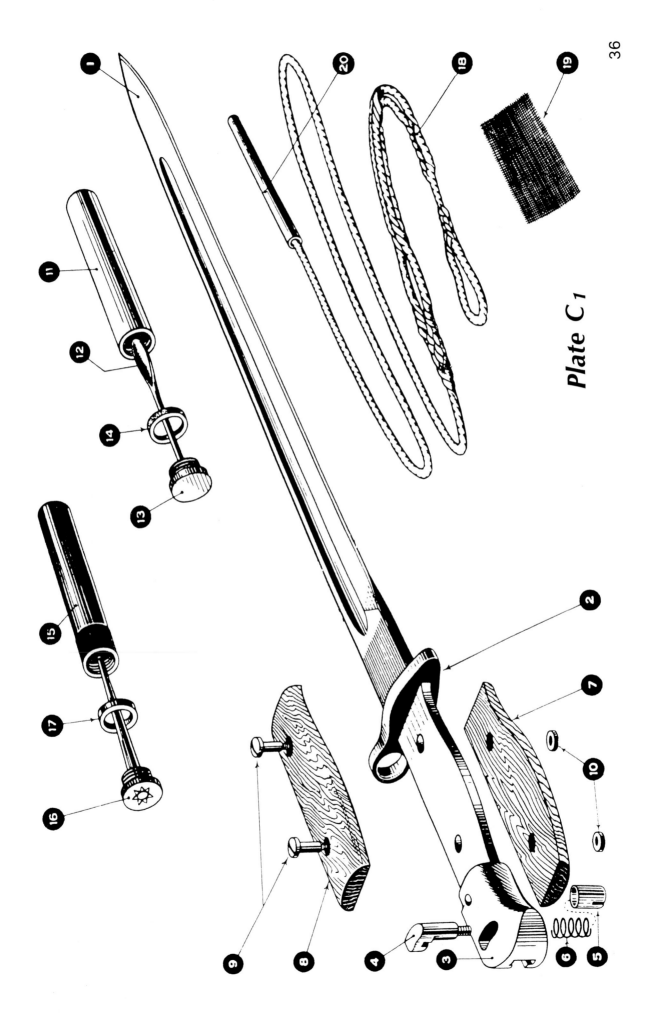

Plate C₁

Plate C1

REF. NO.	DESIGNATION		VOCAB. NUMBER	MAT.	NO. OFF	DRAWING NUMBER	REMARKS
	RIFLE, No. 1 Mk III, ACCESSORIES						
...	**BAYONET, No. 1 Mk I**	*	BA 0022 A			SAID 2474	Pattern 1907.
C1	BLADE		...	Steel	1	SAID 2474	
2	CROSS-PIECE		...	Steel	1	SAID 2474	
3	POMMEL Brazed to blade		...	Steel	1	SAID 2474	
4	BOLT	*	BB 0024	Steel	1	SAID 2474	
5	NUT	*	BB 0033	Steel	1	SAID 2474	
6	SPRING	*	BB 0036	Steel	1	SAID 2474	
7	GRIP, left } pair	*	BB 0025	Wood	1	SAID 2474	
8	GRIP, right } pair			Wood	1	SAID 2474	
9	SCREW, securing grip	*	BB 0035	Steel	2	SAID 2474	
10	NUT	*	BB 0034	Steel	2	SAID 2474	
...	**BOTTLE, OIL, Mk IV**	*	BA 0053 A			ADD(S) 360	Australian drawing.
11	BODY		...	Brass	1	ADD(S) 360	
12	SPOON	*	BB 0054	Steel	1	ADD(S) 357	
13	STOPPER	*	BB 0055	Brass	1	ADD(S) 358	
14	WASHER	*	BB 0056	Leather	1	ADD(S) 359	
or							
...	**BOTTLE, OIL, Mk V**	*	BA 6320 A			DD(E) 2562	British drawing.
15	BODY		...	Plastic	1	DD(E) 2562 -1	
16	STOPPER, with rod	*	BB 6321	Plastic	1	DD(E) 2562 -4	
17	WASHER, hand, front	*	BB 6326 ‡	Leather	1	DD(E) 2562 -3	
	PULL-THROUGH, SINGLE, Mk IV, "A" or "B"						
...		*	...			SAID 257E	
18	CORD, single	*	BB 0520	Cord	1	SAID 257E	
19	GAUZE (not with "B" pull-through)	*	BB 0521	Steel	1	SAID 257E	
20	WEIGHT	*	BB 0522	Brass	1	SAID 257E	

‡ Pull-through, single, Mk IV, "A" BA 0517

‡ Pull-through, single, Mk IV, "B" BA 0518

* Indicates component part available for Workshop replacement.

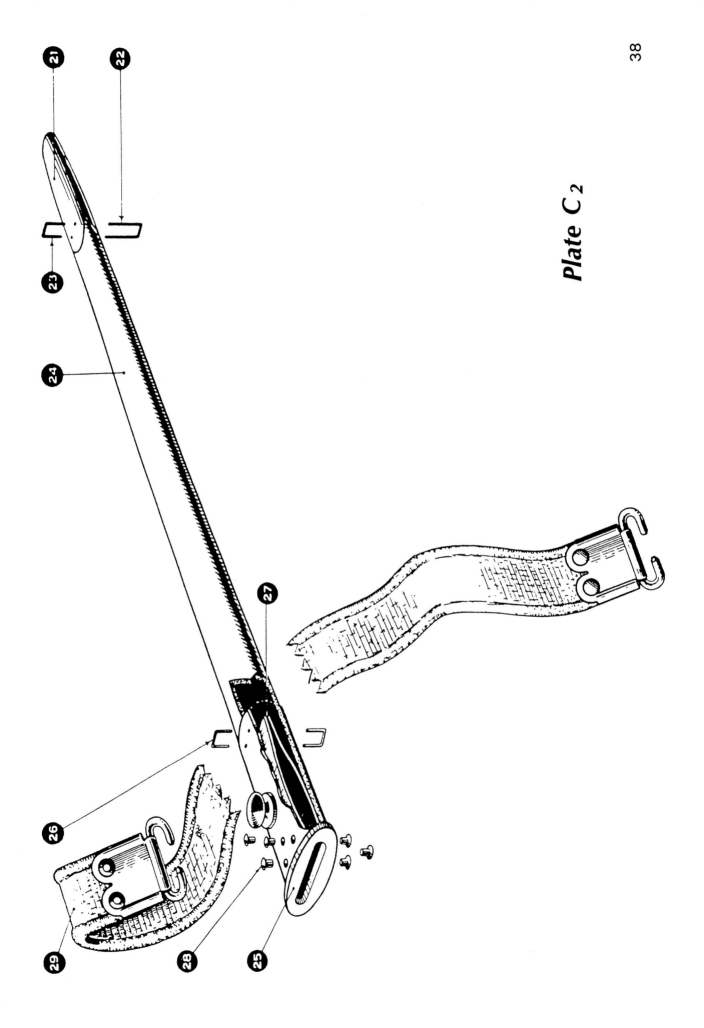

Plate C₂

REF. NO.	DESIGNATION	VOCAB. NUMBER	MAT.	NO. OFF	DRAWING NUMBER	REMARKS
Plate C2						
	RIFLE, No. 1 Mk III, ACCESSORIES					
	SCABBARD, BAYONET, No. 1 Mk II *	BA 1211 A				
C 21	CHAPE . . . *	BB 1212	Steel		SAID 2474	
22	LACE, long, .056" dia.x 1.35" wire *	BB 1213	Mild Steel	1	SAID 2474	
23	LACE, short, .056" dia.x 1.05" wire *	BB 1214	Mild Steel	1	SAID 2474	
24	LEATHER . . . *	BB 8353	Leather		SAID 2474	
25	LOCKET . . . *	BB 1216	Steel	1	SAID 2474	
26	LACE, short, .056" dia.x 1.05" wire *	BB 1214	Mild Steel	2	SAID 2474	
27	SPRING . . .	. . .	Steel	2	SAID 2474	
28	RIVET . . .	. . .	Mild Steel	6	SAID 2474	
29	SLING, rifle, web (complete) .	AA 1657	Web	1	SAID 2474	46-in. in length. SMG & LMG sling is 11-in. longer at 57-in. overall, Part no. CAA 3600

*   Indicates component part available for Workshop replacement.

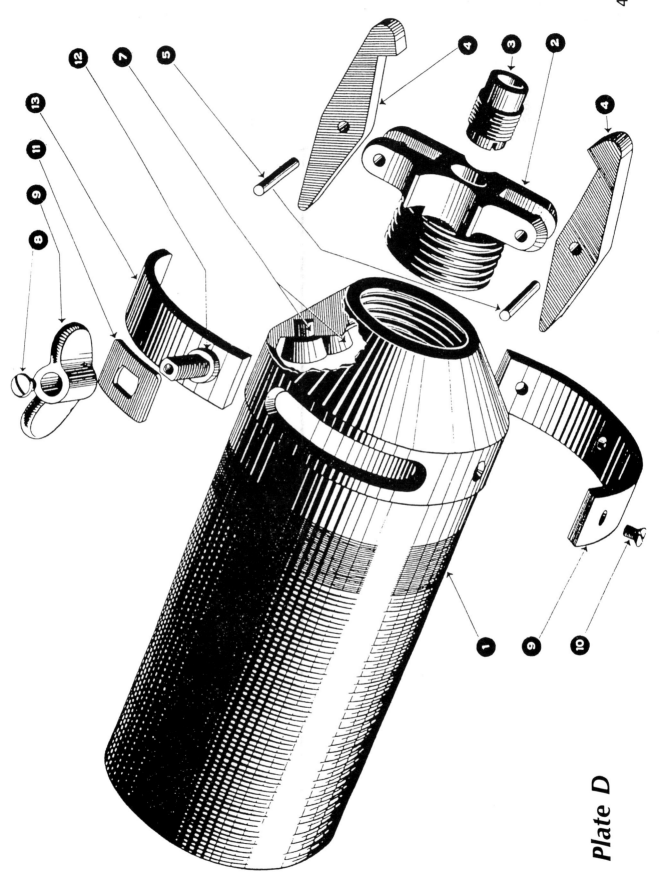

Plate D

Plate D

REF. NO.	DESIGNATION	VOCAB. NUMBER	MAT.	NO. OFF	DRAWING NUMBER	REMARKS
	DISCHARGER, GRENADE, RIFLE, NO. 1 MK I, 2½-in.					
D 1	BARREL	BA 0100 GA	. . .	1	AID 1434/C	Commercially made by contractors rather than government small arms factories, and usually proprietary as such.
2	BASE	. . .	Mild Steel	1	AID 1434/C	
3	SCREW, adjusting	. . .	Mild Steel	1	AID 1434/C	
4	LEVER	. . .	Mild Steel	2	AID 1434/C	
5	PIN	. . .	Steel	2	AID 1434/C	
6	NUT, wing, B.S.W., 3/16"	G1/GAA 5852	Mild Steel	1	AID 1434/C	Hardware item.
7	PEG, steel	. . .	Mild Steel	2	AID 1434/C	
8	SCREW, keep	. . .	Mild Steel	1	AID 1434/C	
9	SEGMENT, fixed	. . .	Mild Steel	1	AID 1434/C	
10	SCREW, fixing (or) Rivet	. . .	Mild Steel	3	AID 1434/C	
11	SEGMENT, moving	. . .	Mild Steel	1	AID 1434/C	
12	STUD, screwed	. . .	Mild Steel	1	AID 1434/C	
13	WASHER	. . .	Spring Steel	1	AID 1434/C	

The deficiency of Vocabulary Nos. for the individual components (except for the wing nut) would indicate that these parts were not maintained by the ordnance stores system as regular spares. Also, the same drawing number applies to all parts. These discharger cups are usually marked with the contractor's name or initials; they all appear to have been produced by commercial contractors, distinct from the government ordnance factories. Service examples were marked with the "broad arrow" upon acceptance into government service.

STRIPPING & ASSEMBLY

A PRACTICAL GUIDE

The armourers' trade was a specialist one which usually entailed years of instruction as an apprentice and then posting to ordnance workshops or a specialist corps unit. Training on the various rifles, pistols, bayonets and machine guns required years of practice and the skills were usually passed down by the more experienced, veteran armourers. Set procedures were applied for even the most basic operations in the daily maintenance and servicing of military arms. Many ex-service weapons in private collections, museums, and available on the market today have been abused or damaged by improper stripping, faulty servicing or careless repair. No collector or museum staff could hope to learn the armourer's trade in a short space of time, but most poor workmanship and abuse can be avoided by following some simple rules, and using a little thought and deliberation.

Values of ex-military and collectors' firearms and edged weapons are significantly reduced where the wooden furniture has been cracked, screw heads burred, threads stripped, parts marked by improper use of a vice or stillson wrench, or components broken or lost. This is more unfortunate when the item has intrinsic value or is a scarce model, and the damage has been caused by pure negligence. In this section, the stripping and assembly related to the S.M.L.E. is examined, although most of the principles apply to other firearms as well.

Knowledge and the use of proper tools are the two prime elements. For the former, a gunsmith or armourer could be asked; or maybe a service manual or suitable reference consulted. Regarding the latter, many armourers' tools and gunsmithing implements are available on the market today and this section here is intended to address that issue.

Before even seeking out any original or replica military armourers' tools, a good set of screwdrivers, a vice with wooden or soft metal jaw inserts, quality punches, a copper or rawhide mallet, and sharp chisels are advisable. Screwdrivers should have good square edges, hollow ground tips are even better, if available. And a few different sizes are necessary so as to obtain a good tight fit in the screwdriver slot of the screw head, for the full width of the slot. This is especially important for removing tight or seized screws. Penetrating lubricant can also be useful in these circumstances.

Specialist armourers tools are usually required for tasks such as removing the firing pin, extractor spring, leather stock bolt wad in the butt, dial sight pivot screw, and the backsight slide catch screw. Headspace gauges, striker protrusion gauges, spring weighing gauges and foresight cramps are not required by most collectors or museums today, unless the rifles are likely to be used or fired.

A summary of the 1917 Ordnance College manual follows, including most details required for routine stripping and assembly of the S.M.L.E. rifle. But first, some tips for the novice.

In order to unscrew the stock bolt and remove the butt of S.M.L.E (No. 1) rifles, the stock fore-end MUST BE REMOVED FIRST. The stock bolt has a squared end which fits into a plate at the rear of the fore-end (see Items 36 & 37, Plate B2). Any serious attempt to unscrew the stock bolt first is likely to cause the fixed plate to split the fore-end. In some cases, the safety catch spring screw may protrude through the steel butt socket, into the butt itself; so it may require unscrewing for a few turns to release the butt stock.

Centre-punching was employed to secure certain screws on some rifles. Screws such as the backsight bed screws (S.M.L.E. Marks I, I*, II and II* only), aperture sight spring screw, nosecap front screw, sear screw and the front trigger guard screw. These can usually be removed with an appropriate, properly-fitting screwdriver. However, should the screw still be difficult to turn, a small pin punch (fitted along the screwdriver slot) may be hit with a hammer to push back any burring which prevents the screw head from turning.

Screws for the outer bands and swivels should be inserted from the left side of the rifle. The extended (longer) side of the sling swivel should be positioned so that the long side is to the right, facing the same side as the bolt handle. This is reported to have been so that the rifle would carry better over the shoulder, especially whilst mounted on horseback.

Collectors are all too often indifferent regarding safety procedures and common courtesies with firearms. When first handled, any firearm should have its action opened and the chamber and magazine inspected for ammunition. Common courtesy also dictates that the muzzle should be pointed up or down, and not in the direction of any other person.

STRIPPING SEQUENCE — *per 1917 Ordnance College Manual.*

Remove rear handguard: Hold rifle in the left hand. Raise sight, use tool No. 1 as lever, and assist to ease off with fingers and thumb of left hand. Care must be taken to avoid splitting the handguard.

To perform the stripping correctly and to avoid any damage, the rifle is best clamped in a bench vice as shown. The vice jaws should be covered with wood or soft metal so as to avoid marking the rifle. Rifle positions for clamping and the use of an additional stay or support in each position, are as per the illustrations.

1st Position.

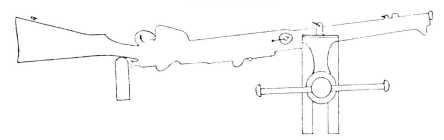

Remove nosecap screws: Back and front, remove weaker (smaller) screw last.
Remove nosecap: Tap off towards muzzle, with suitable piece of wood applied against the sword-bar of the nosecap.
Remove outer band screw, swivel and outer band: Using screwdriver.
Remove front handguard: No tool required, merely lift off.

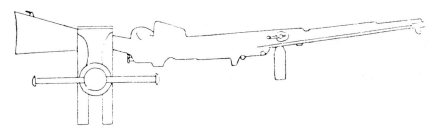

Undo inner band screw: This screw may be left in the fore-end.
Remove magazine: Release magazine catch and remove magazine.
Remove trigger guard screws: Back and front, remove weaker (smaller) screw last.
Remove trigger guard: Lift trigger guard out of seating in fore-end.
Remove stock, fore-end: To be lifted level, raising the front end through medium of spring and stud, fore-end. If fore-end is tight to remove, tap rear end lightly with wooden drift, taking care not to crush or mark the fore-end wood.

3RD POSITION.

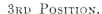

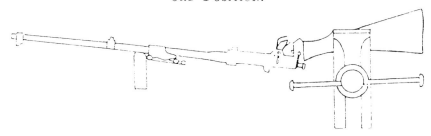

Remove sear spring: Place large screwdriver between magazine catch and spring, and turn counter-clockwise.
Remove sear screw with bolthead retaining spring: May be secured by centre-punching.
Remove sear: Lift out.
Remove magazine catch pin and catch: Using drift or pin punch.
Remove magazine cut-off screw and cut-off: With cut-off in the open position, ease out by applying screwdriver between the arm of cut-off and body.
Remove buttplate screw and butt-plate: Using large screwdriver for the butt screws.
Remove stock bolt wad: Using tool, removing wad, stock-bolt.
Remove stock bolt: The action body should be held whilst unscrewing bolt. Immediately the bolt jumps, indicating it is free, stop turning, otherwise the square end of the bolt will damage the threads.
Remove butt: If this is tight, grasp the rifle with one hand near the backsight and the other at the butt-stock wrist. Tap the butt smartly, about 3 inches from the heel, on a wood surface or block, at the same time pulling outwards with both hands. The greatest care must be taken to ensure that the stock bolt is free of the body before doing this.

4TH POSITION.

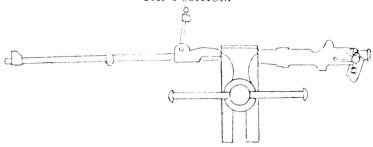

Remove long range aperture sight spring screw, and aperture sight.
Remove locking bolt with safety catch: And unscrew safety catch from locking bolt.
Remove breech bolt: Raise bolt handle as far as possible and draw back as far as possible. Then turn bolt head upwards (90°) and draw the bolt clear. Rifles fitted with sliding charger guides (S.M.L.E. Marks I and II series) necessitate the slide being drawn to the rear to allow the bolt head to be turned vertical.

SIGHT. Only to be removed for special instruction or repair.
Remove pin, fixing washer, and washer: Use drift (pin punch). This pin is tapered.
Remove pin, axis, backsight, and sight leaf: Use drift (pin punch).
Remove screw, spring, back sight: Use correct screwdriver, per bolthead extractor screw.
Remove spring, backsight: This is dovetailed in; special tool required to remove it.

ASSEMBLY. Replace in the reverse order described heretofore. Special regard as follows:
Backsight leaf axis pin: Replaced from left to right, using a pilot pin to give it a lead.
Breech bolt: Check that bolt head is screwed home, that the cocking piece, resisting lug, and extractor are all in the vertical plane. To replace, reverse the removal procedure.
Bolt locking with safety catch: Place catch on stem of locking bolt at 9 o'clock. Use no force whatsoever, and be careful to prevent the catch from sagging when trying to engage the threads. When screwed home correctly, it should be at 10.30 position.
Cut-off screw: Screw down flush.
Sear spring: Engage the long arm with the notch on sear, then place a screwdriver against the nib on the short arm, and press gently down until it engages the notch on the magazine catch.
Stock, fore-end: Carefully examine fore-end to see that all its fittings are in position. See that the square end on stock bolt is correct and the inner band adjusted before attempting to place the fore-end on.
Trigger guard screws: Fix the back screw first.
Magazine: On Nos. 1, 2 & 3 magazines, check that the stop clip is turned up before attempting to replace in rifle.
Inner band: Spring should have slight play when the screw is tightened up (test by pressure with large screwdriver).
Nosecap: Keep the rear end of nosecap down to ensure screws engaging correctly.
Sling swivels: Short side to the left, same side as dial sight. Long side to right, same side as the breech bolt handle.

Stripping of the magazine, breech bolt and backsight completes the normal maintenance procedure. Removal of the barrel requires special action wrench and bench vice fitted with knox form dies. Use of a flat lever through boltway is likely to twist the action body.

MAGAZINE: Depress rear end of platform and draw the front end clear of magazine behind the front lip. *(Magazines Nos. 1, 2 & 3 require stop clip at front right to be turned).* Then ease the platform (and attached spring) out to the front, twisting it slightly to the right, drawing it forward out of the case. Ease the auxiliary spring off the front of case.

BREECH BOLT: Remove charger guide stop *(Marks I, I*, II & II* rifles only).* Remove extractor spring with punch end of correct tool; cover with thumb to prevent spring flying out. Remove extractor screw and extractor from bolthead. With suitable coin or screwdriver, remove striker keeper screw from cocking piece. Remove bolthead with striker, mainspring and cocking piece, ensuring that the stud on cocking piece is in the long cam. Striker removal tool (tube spanner type with nibs to engage in striker slots) was used for unscrewing a tight striker from the cocking piece.

BACKSIGHT: Remove slide catch screw and spring with fork screw driver (for dial sight). Remove slide and catch by pressing the catch to disengage worm from rack and draw slide off leaf. Remove worm catch slide from slide using a drift, pressing catch with worm outwards. The worm axis pin and worm could then be removed if repair was required. The wind-gauge screw head fixing pin (not on S.M.L.E. Mk III*) could then be removed with a drift; this pin is tapered. After this, the wind-gauge head screw and spring could be removed, and a small screwdriver used to remove the wind-gauge screw. Then the wind-gauge and spring could also be removed.

Sourcing Lee-Enfield tools and component spares can be difficult. Certain gunshops may well have some of these items, but they are often reluctant to supply them as they are not always easy to replace. Local collectors recommend Brian Labudda's Lee Spares (P.O. Box 770, Kingaroy, Australia 4610; fax 07 4162 3257 or international +61 7 4162 3257) as a likely source for many of these tools and Lee-Enfield parts.

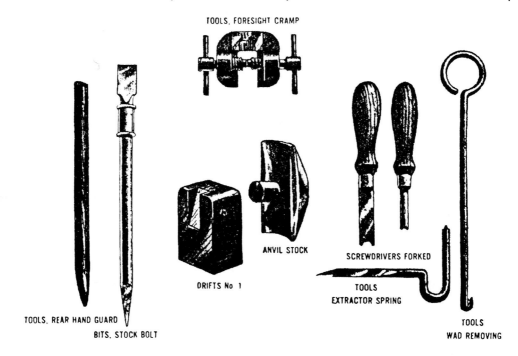

TOOLS, FORESIGHT CRAMP

ANVIL STOCK

SCREWDRIVERS FORKED

DRIFTS No 1

TOOLS
EXTRACTOR SPRING

TOOLS, REAR HAND GUARD

BITS, STOCK BOLT

TOOLS
WAD REMOVING

HEADSPACING and GAUGING

This is effected with headspace gauges and two such gauges are usually sufficient; termed "GO" and "NO-GO". The GO gauge is .067-in while the NO-GO is .074-in. With the GO gauge in the chamber and the bolt being closed, it should "firm up" or just close when the bolt handle is being lowered to its normal position for firing. The bolt should not close on the NO-GO gauge. These and other tools are shown on page 370 of the *Lee-Enfield Story*.

To adjust headspace on the No. 1 rifle was not as straightforward as for its successor, the No. 4. Sets of numbered, sized boltheads were not available for the No. 1 rifle. The usual method was to measure bolthead length with good calipers or a gauge, from the bolt-face to the back, where the threaded portion starts. Should the appropriately sized bolthead not be available from the "spare bolt-head box", a slightly oversize one was chosen and rubbed down with a circular motion on lubricated emery paper, until firm on the GO gauge.

PARTS MANUFACTURE IDENTIFICATION

A close examination of the inspector's marks on component parts will help establish the authenticity of a rifle as different letter indicators were applied by the various factories. Some inspection marks on pre-war rifles differ from those used later, and so subsequent replacement parts may be identified. Many rifles had parts replaced in service, in the course of routine maintenance and repair. Totally original specimens with no replacement parts are not often encountered as the .303 rifles were in service for many years.

Receiver Manufacturer Markings: The S.M.L.E. rifles were marked on the butt socket with the factory and production or conversion year. British rifles will be found to have ENFIELD, SPARKBROOK, B.S.A. or L.S.A. marks, indicating manufacture at the government Enfield or Sparkbrook establishments, or the commercial Birmingham Small Arms or London Small Arms factories. Great War British "peddled scheme" rifles have no maker's name on the butt socket, only a G.R. cypher and the year 1916, 1917 or 1918. The factory name, SSA or NRF on these rifles will be found at the top, rear of the receiver body, near the safety catch and boltway. Such rifles were marked with Enfield inspection marks. See the *Lee-Enfield Story* pages 153-154 for illustrated details.

Australian production was marked LITHGOW. Indian factory marks vary but ISHAPORE was marked until the late 1930's after which the factory mark usually comprised GRI and later, RFI. *Lee-Enfield Story* pages 479-496 lists of the various markings. Chapters 9 and 10 detail the Indian and Australian production and their action body marking styles.

Parts & Inspectors' Markings: These indicate the passing of inspection and also identify where that particular examination was carried out. Examples of these marks are listed in *Lee-Enfield Story*, pages 490-495; some are shown here for ready reference. In most cases, the inspectors' stamps incorporate a number. The number indicated a particular inspector, and therefore each inspector could be identified by his individual number. The examples here are only typical; the form of these stamps may be found to differ in that the letter indicator may be above the inspector's number or vice versa. Australian inspection stamps often use an arrow rather than a crown at top. Inspection marks should not be confused with proof marks which incorporate crossed flags, or factory identification codes.

Enfield Inspector's mark:	♔ E 12	*Early Lithgow Inspector's mark:*	☆ A
Sparkbrook Inspector's mark:	♔ B 5	*Lithgow View mark:*	☆ A VI
B.S.A. Inspector's mark:	♔ ß 16	*Lithgow Inspector's mark:*	L ↑ 2
L.S.A Inspector's mark:	♔ X 8	*Orange Inspector's mark:*	O ↑ 1
Birmingham Repair Inspector's mark:	♔ BR 3	*Sydney Inspector's mark:*	♔ 2 S
Ishapore Inspector's mark:	♔ GRI 12	*Post-war Ishapore Inspector's mark:*	I S 7 B